BY JANE BOWLES

Two Serious Ladies (novel) (1943)

In the Summer House (play) (1954)

Plain Pleasures (stories) (1966)

The Collected Works of Jane Bowles (1966)

Jane Bowles

FEMININE WILES

Introduction by
TENNESSEE WILLIAMS

BLACK SPARROW PRESS · SANTA BARBARA · 1976

Grateful thanks is due the editors of *Antaeus* and *Paris Review* where "Andrew", "Emmy Moore's Journal", and "Going to Massachusetts" originally appeared (the latter under the title "The Courtship of Janet Murphy"). Thanks is also due Lawrence D. Stewart for the use of two of the photographs of Jane Bowles reproduced in this volume, and to Robert A. Wilson and George Bixby for information and assistance. Finally, this volume was made possible by Paul Bowles, who conceived the project, and who collected and edited all the material.

The frontispiece drawing of Jane Bowles is by Marguerite McBey and was done in Tangier in 1963.

LIBRARY OF CONGRESS CATALOGING IN PUBLICATION DATA

Bowles, Jane Auer, 1917-1973.
  Feminine wiles.

  CONTENTS: Stories & sketches: Andrew. Emmy Moore's journal. Going to Massachusetts. "Curls and a quiet country place." — Play: At the Jumping Bean. — A group of photographs. — Six letters
  I. Title.
PS3503.0837F4 1976   818'.5'209   76-8424
ISBN 0-87685-253-3
ISBN 0-87685-252-5 pbk.

"But I will have no truck with feminine wiles."

Persons of note and / or notoriety in the literary and entertainment worlds are often asked to give what are called "quotes" concerning the work of a writer, and often these solicited "quotes" are more in keeping with the market-place than with honesty of statement.

I was never asked to express an opinion of the work of Jane Bowles. I read it, and exclaimed my opinion of it as spontaneously as if I'd stumbled into a wonderland of new, totally fresh sensibility—which, indeed, I had.

I knew Mrs. Bowles personally, but it was not her unique charm as a person that drew from me the opinions which I hold regarding her work. I consider her the most important writer of prose fiction in modern American letters without reference to my close, intuitive friendship with her, and my knowledge of her physical disabilities and spiritual torment during her last years.

Her work doesn't need an appreciation influenced by sympathy with the circumstances of her life. Of course her work was the heart of her life, but it deserves to be appraised as if you had never known her, and it is fully able to stand undiminished by this detached view.

Now having confirmed, unconditionally, my first and lasting opinion of Jane Bowles's work, which doesn't need my opinion, I may speak of her as the totally original and delightful person that she was.

The very first time I met Jane was in Acapulco the summer of 1940; but that was so briefly and so long ago that I have no impression of it except that, except that Janie was totally concerned, it seemed to me, with what you could eat safely in Acapulco at that time, which was practically nothing.

Then, in December 1948, I met her when she came aboard the Vulcania, *anchored for debarkation in the Strait of Gibraltar, in the presence of Paul Bowles, her husband, and my friend Frank Merlo.*

In appearance she was a lovely girl, small, piquant, darting between humor, anxiety, love and distraction. I had met nervous girls before, but her quicksilver animation, her continual cries, to me and herself: "Shall we do this or shall we do that? What shall we do?" showed such an extreme kind of excited indecision that I was skeptical of its reality—intrigued, certainly, but still somewhat incredulous.

Used to it as Paul must have been, he stood there, simply smiling in a bemused sort of way. It seems to me that Frank Merlo took command of the chaotic situation, much to the relief of us all. (Of course, Paul may already have known how things would go, but was simply waiting for the accustomed flurry to subside.)

Frank saw that the car was put onto the European shore; we settled down for the night at the Rock Hotel in Gib.

"Is she for real?" I asked Frank, when we had retired.

"Are you for real?" he countered, a little grimly, perhaps.

I wasn't sure about that, but I soon came to see the reality of Jane. All the indecision was a true and dreadful concern that she might suggest a wrong move in a world that she had correctly surmised to be so inclined to turn wrongly.

There were many subsequent meetings, in Tangier, Paris and New York. What most impressed me about Jane, the person, was her concern for others, for their comfort and their entertainment. The important little things, especially such as providing meals, acquainting you with the right doctors in foreign places, conducting you through markets, introducing you to the interesting people, and somehow, in the midst of confusion, finding the precisely right words to reassure you in your own confusion—these were her particular gifts—ways to get agreeably through day and evening.

* * *

Her work, her life: deep truth, observed without pretension, with humor and humanity.

As artist and person, an angel.

Tennessee Williams
Nov. 11, 1974

TABLE OF CONTENTS

STORIES & SKETCHES

The fictional pieces collected here are fragments of longer, unfinished works, taken from the author's notebooks. They date from the 1940's and 1950's.

Andrew

Andrew's mother looked at her son's face. "He wants to get away from us," she thought, "and he will." She felt overcome by a mortal fatigue. "He simply wants to spring out of his box into the world." With a flippant and worldly gesture she described a flight through the air. Then abruptly she burst into tears and buried her face in her hands.

Andrew watched her thin shoulders shaking inside her woollen dress. When his mother cried he felt as though his face were made of marble. He could not accept the weeping as a part of her personality. It did not appear to be the natural climax of a mood. Instead it seemed to descend upon her from somewhere far away, as if she were giving voice to the crying of a child in some distant place. For it was the crying of a creature many years younger than she, a disgrace for which he felt responsible, since it was usually because of him that she cried.

There was nothing he could say to console her because she was right. He wanted to go away, and there was nothing else he wanted at all. "It's natural when you're young to want to go away," he would say to himself, but it did not help; he always felt that his own desire to escape was different from that of others. When he was in a good humor he would go about feeling that he and many others too were *all* going away. On such days his face was smooth and he enjoyed his life, although even then he was not communicative. More than anything he wanted all days to be like those rare free ones when he went about whistling and enjoying every simple thing he did. But he had to work hard to get such days, because of his inner conviction that his own going away was like no other going away in the world, a certainty he found it impossible to dislodge. He was right, of course, but from a very early age his life had been devoted to his struggle to rid himself of his feeling of uniqueness. With the years he was becoming more expert at travesty, so that now his mother's crying was more destructive. Watching her cry now, he was more convinced than ever that he was not like other boys who wanted to go away. The truth bit into him harder, for seeing her he could not believe even faintly that he shared his sin with other young men. He and his mother were isolated, sharing the same disgrace, and because of this sharing, separated from one another. His life was truly miserable compared to the lives of other boys, and he knew it.

When his mother's sobs had quieted down somewhat, his father called the waitress and asked for the check. "That's good tomato soup," he told her. "And ham with Hawaiian pineapple is one of my favorites, as you know." The waitress did not answer, and the engaging expression on his face slowly faded.

They pushed their chairs back and headed for the cloakroom. When they were outside Andrew's father suggested that they walk to the summit of the sloping lawn where some cannonballs were piled in the shape of a pyramid. "We'll go over to the cannonballs," he said. "Then we'll come back."

They struggled up the hill in the teeth of a bitterly cold wind, holding on to their hats. "This is the north, folks!" his father shouted into the gale. "It's hard going at times, but in a hot climate no one develops."

Andrew put his foot against one of the cannonballs. He could feel the cold iron through the sole of his shoe.

*   *   *

He had applied for a job in a garage, but he was inducted into the Army before he knew whether or not they had accepted his application. He loved being in the Army, and even took pleasure in the nickname which his hutmates had given him the second day after his arrival. He was called Buttonlip; because of this name he talked even less than usual. In general he hated to talk and could not imagine talking as being a natural expression of a man's thoughts. This was not shyness, but secretiveness.

One day in the Fall he set out on a walk through the pine grove surrounding the camp. Soon he sniffed smoke and stopped walking. "Someone's making a fire," he said to himself. Then he continued on his way. It was dusk in the grove, but beyond, outside, the daylight was still bright. Very shortly he reached a clearing. A young soldier sat there, crouched over a fire which he was feeding with long twigs. Andrew thought he recognized him—he too was undoubtedly a recent arrival—and so his face was not altogether unfamiliar.

14

The boy greeted Andrew with a smile and pointed to a tree trunk that lay on the ground nearby. "Sit down," he said. "I'm going to cook dinner. The mess sergeant gives me my stuff uncooked when I want it that way so I can come out here and make a campfire."

Andrew had an urge to bolt from the clearing, but he seated himself stiffly on the end of the tree trunk. The boy was beautiful, with an Irish-American face and thick curly brown hair. His cheeks were blood red from the heat of the flames. Andrew looked at his face and fell in love with him. Then he could not look away.

A mess kit and a brown paper package lay on the ground. "My food is there in that brown bag," the boy said. "I'll give you a little piece of meat so you can see how good it tastes when it's cooked here, out in the air. Did you go in for bonfires when you were a kid?"

"No," said Andrew. "Too much wind," he added, some vague memory stirring in his mind.

"There's lots of wind," he agreed, and Andrew was unreasonably delighted that the boy considered his remark a sensible one. "Lots of wind, but that never need stop you." He looked up at Andrew with a bright smile. "Not if you like a fire and the outdoors. Where I worked they used to call me Outdoor Tommy. Nobody got sore."

Andrew was so disarmed by his charm that he did not find the boy's last statement odd until he had heard the sentence repeated several times inside his head.

"Sore?"

"Yes, sore." He untied the string that bound his food package and set the meat on a little wire grate. "They never got sore at me," he repeated, measuring his words. "They were a right nice bunch. Sometimes guys don't take to it if you like something real well. They get sore. These guys didn't get sore. Never. They saw me going off to the woods with my supper every evening, and sometimes even, one or two of them would come along. And sometimes twenty-five of us would go out with steaks. But mostly I just went by myself and they stayed back playing games in the cottages or going into town. If it had been winter I'd have stayed in the cottages more. I was never there in winter. If I had been, I might have gone out anyway. I like to make a fire in the snow."

"Where were you?" asked Andrew.

15

"In a factory by a stream." The meat was cooked, and he cut off a tiny piece for Andrew. "This is all you're going to get. Otherwise I won't have enough in me."

"I've eaten. With the others," said Andrew shortly.

"You've got to try this," the boy insisted. "And see if you like eating it this way, cooked on the coals outdoors. Then maybe you can get on the good side of the mess sergeant and bring your food out here, too. They're all right here. I could stay in this outfit. Just as good as I could stay back home in the hotel."

"You live in a hotel?"

"I lived in a hotel except the summer I was in the factory."

"Well, I'll see you," Andrew mumbled, walking away.

One night after he had eaten his supper he found himself wandering among the huts on the other side of the mess hall. It was Saturday night and most of the huts were dark. He was dejected, and thought of going into town and drinking beer by himself. Andrew drank only beer because he considered other forms of alcohol too expensive, although most of the other soldiers, who had less money than he, drank whiskey. As he walked along thinking of the beer he heard a voice calling to him. He looked up and saw Tommy standing in the doorway of a hut only a few feet away. They greeted each other, and Tommy motioned to him to wait. Then he went inside to get something.

Andrew leaned against a tree with his hands in his pockets. When Tommy came out he held a flat box in his hand. "Sparklers," he said. "I bought them after the Fourth, cut-rate. It's the best time to buy them."

"That's good to know," said Andrew. He had never touched fireworks except on the day of the Fourth. He had a brief memory of alleys on summer nights, where boys were grinding red devils under their heels in the dark. Compared to him they were poor, and he was therefore, like all well-off children, both revolted by them and envious of them. The fact that they played with fireworks after the Fourth of July was disgusting in a way. It had a foreign flavor, and made him feel a little sick, just as the Irish did, and the Jews, and circus people. But he was also excited by them. The sick feeling was part of the excitement.

Andrew had never dressed as a ragamuffin on Thanksgiving, and he had once almost fainted when two boys disguised as hags had come begging at the door. His father's rage had contributed greatly to the nightmarish quality of the memory. It was usually his mother, and not his father, who was angry. But he remembered that his father had seemed to attach great importance to the custom of masquerading on Thanksgiving. "He should be dressed up himself and out there with the others!" he had cried. "He has no right to be lying there, white as a sheet. There's no earthly reason for it. This is a holiday. It's time for *fun*. My God, doesn't anyone in this house ever have any fun? I was a ragamuffin every year until I was grown. Why doesn't he tear up an old pair of pants and go out? I'll take the crown out of my straw hat if he wants to wear it. But he should go out!"

Quite naturally Andrew had thought of running away. This was one of his worst memories. He hated to hear his father speak about the poor. His own romantic conception of them made his father's democratic viewpoint unacceptable. It was as incongruous as if he had come into the parlor and found his father offering one of his cigarettes to a pirate or a gypsy. He preferred his mother's disdain for the poor. In fact, she liked nothing but the smell of her intimates. Of course, she made him feel sick, too, but sick in a different way.

"Come on. Take one," Tommy was saying, and he lighted a sparkler. Andrew stared at the needle-like sparks. The hissing sound of the sparkler awakened old sick feelings, and he longed to pull the little stick from between Tommy's fingers and bury the bright sparks in the earth. Instead, he looked gloomy and said nothing. He liked the fact that Tommy was poor, but he did not want him to be so poor that he seemed foreign. Then he realized that others might not see a connection between being a foreigner and playing with sparklers after the Fourth of July, and he was aware that there was really no logical connection. Yet he himself felt that there was one. Sometimes he wondered whether or not other people went about pretending to be logical while actually they felt as he did inside, but this was not very often, since he usually took it for granted that everyone was more honest than he. The fact that it was impossible to say anything of all this to Tommy both depressed and irritated him.

"I saved a whole box of sparklers for you," Tommy said. "I thought you'd be coming to the clearing."

Andrew could not believe he was hearing the words. At the same time his heart had begun to beat faster. He told himself that he must retain a natural expression.

"I don't know if you like to fool around with stuff they make for kids," Tommy went on. "Maybe you think it's not worth your while. But you don't have to pay much attention to these. You light 'em and they burn themselves out. You can swing 'em around and talk at the same time. Or you don't even have to swing 'em. You can stick 'em in the ground and they go on all by themselves, like little pinwheels. There's not much point to 'em, but I get 'em anyway, every summer after the Fourth of July is over with. This isn't the box I saved for you. That one I gave to someone else who had a nephew." He handed the box to Andrew.

Andrew's face was like stone and his mouth was drawn.

"Here." Tommy tapped the back of Andrew's hand with the flat box. "Here are your sparklers."

"No," said Andrew. "I don't want any sparklers." He was not going to offer any explanation for refusing them. Tommy did not seem to want one in any case. He went on tracing designs in the night with his sparkler. "I'll just stash this box away if you don't want 'em. I can use 'em up. It's better to have one of these going than nothing, and sometimes there's no time for me to build a bonfire."

"You take things easy, don't you?" Andrew said.

Emmy Moore's Journal

On certain days I forget why I'm here. Today once again I wrote my husband all my reasons for coming. He encouraged me to come each time I was in doubt. He said that the worst danger for me was a state of vagueness, so I wrote telling him why I had come to the Hotel Henry—my eighth letter on this subject—but with each new letter I strengthen my position. I am reproducing the letter here. Let there be no mistake. My journal is intended for publication. I want to publish for glory, but also in order to aid other women. This is the letter to my husband, Paul Moore, to whom I have been married sixteen years. (I am childless.) He is of North Irish descent, and a very serious lawyer. Also a solitary and lover of the country. He knows all mushrooms, bushes and trees, and he is interested in geology. But these interests do not exclude me. He is sympathetic towards me, and kindly. He wants very much for me to be happy, and worries because I am not. He knows everything about me, including how much I deplore being the feminine kind of woman that I am. In fact, I am unusually feminine for an American of Anglo stock. (Born in Boston.) I am almost a "Turkish" type. Not physically, at least not entirely, because though fat I have ruddy Scotch cheeks and my eyes are round and not slanted or almond-shaped. But sometimes I feel certain that I exude an atmosphere very similar to theirs (the Turkish women's) and then I despise myself. I find the women in my country so extraordinarily manly and independent, capable of leading regiments, or of fending for themselves on desert islands if necessary. (These are poor examples, but I am getting my point across.) For me it is an experience simply to have come here alone to the Hotel Henry and to eat my dinner and lunch by myself. If possible before I die, I should like to become a little more independent, and a little less Turkish than I am now. Before I go any further, I had better say immediately that I mean no offense to Turkish women. They are probably busy combating the very same Turkish quality in themselves that I am controlling in me. I understand, too (though this is irrelevant), that many Turkish women are beautiful, and I think that they have discarded their veils. Any other American woman would be sure of this. She would know one way or the other whether the veils had been discarded, whereas I am afraid to come out with a definite statement. I have a feeling that they really have got rid of their veils, but I won't swear to it. Also, if they have done so, I have no idea when they did. Was it many years ago or recently?

Here is my letter to Paul Moore, my husband, in which there is more about Turkish women. Since I am writing this journal with a view to publication, I do not want to ramble on as though I had all the space in the world. No publisher will attempt printing an *enormous* journal written by an unknown woman. It would be too much of a financial risk. Even I, with my ignorance of all matters pertaining to business, know this much. But they may print a small one.

My letter (written yesterday, the morrow of my drunken evening in the Blue Bonnet Room when I accosted the society salesman):

Dearest Paul:

I cannot simply live out my experiment here at the Hotel Henry without trying to justify or at least explain in letters my reasons for being here, and with fair regularity. You encouraged me to write whenever I felt I needed to clarify my thoughts. But you did tell me that I must not feel the need to *justify* my actions. However, I *do* feel the need to justify my actions, and I am certain that until the prayed-for metamorphosis has occurred I shall go on feeling just this need. Oh, how well I know that you would interrupt me at this point and warn me against expecting too much. So I shall say in lieu of metamorphosis, the prayed-for *improvement.* But until then I must justify myself every day. Perhaps you will get a letter every day. On some days the need to write lodges itself in my throat like a cry that must be uttered.

As for the Turkish problem, I am coming to it. You must understand that I am an admirer of Western civilization; that is, of the women who are members of this group. I feel myself that I fall short of being a member, that by some curious accident I was not born in Turkey but should have been. Because of my usual imprecision I cannot even tell how many countries belong to what we call Western Civilization, but I believe Turkey is the place where East meets West, isn't it? I can just about imagine the women there, from what I have heard about the country and the pictures I have seen of it. As for being troubled or obsessed by real Oriental women, I am not. (I refer to the Chinese, Japanese, Hindus, and so on.) Naturally I am less concerned with the Far Eastern women because there is no danger of my being like them. (The Turkish women are just near enough.) The Far Eastern ones are so very far away, at the opposite end of the earth, that they could easily be just as independent and masculine as the women of the Western world. The ones living in-between the two masculine areas would be soft and feminine. Naturally I don't believe this for a minute, but still, the real Orientals are so far away and such a mystery to me that it might as well be true. Whatever they are, it couldn't affect me. They look too different from the way I look. Whereas Turkish women don't. (Their figures are exactly like mine, alas!)

Now I shall come to the point. I know full well that you will consider the above discourse a kind of joke. Or if you don't, you will be irritated with me for making statements of such a sweeping and inaccurate nature. For surely you will consider the picture of the world that I present as inaccurate. I myself know that this concept of the women (all three sets—Western, Middle and Eastern) is a puerile one. It could even be called downright idiotic. Yet I assure you that I see things this way, if I relax even a little and look through my own eyes into what is really inside my head. (Though because of my talent for mimicry I am able to simulate looking through the eyes of an educated person when I wish to.) Since I am giving you such a frank picture of myself, I may as well go the whole hog and admit to you that my secret picture of the world is grossly inaccurate. I have completely forgotten to include in it any of the Latin countries. (France, Italy, Spain.) For instance, I have jumped from the Anglo world to the semi-Oriental as if there were no countries in between at all. I know that these exist. (I have even lived in two of them.) But they do not fit into my scheme. I just don't think about the Latins very much, and this is less understandable than my not thinking about the Chinese or Javanese or Japanese women. You can see why without my having to explain it to you. I do know that the French women are more interested in sports than they used to be, and for all I know they may be indistinguishable from Anglo women by now. I haven't been to France recently so I can't be sure. But in any case the women of those countries don't enter into my picture of the world. Or shall I say that the fact of having forgotten utterly to consider them has not altered the way I visualize the division of the world's women? Incredible though it may seem to you, it hasn't altered anything. (My having forgotten all Latin countries, South America included.) I want you to know the whole truth about me. But don't imagine that I wouldn't be capable of concealing my ignorance from you if I wanted to. I am so wily and feminine that I could live by your side for a lifetime and deceive you afresh each day. But I will have no truck with feminine wiles. I know how they can absorb the hours of the day. Many women are delighted to sit around spinning their webs. It is an absorbing occupation, and the women feel they are getting somewhere. And so they are, but only for as long as the man is there to be deceived. And a wily woman alone is a pitiful sight to behold. Naturally.

I shall try to be honest with you so that I can live with you and yet won't be pitiful. Even if tossing my feminine tricks out the window means being left no better than an illiterate backwoodsman, or the bottom fish scraping along the ocean bed, I prefer to have it this way. Now I am too tired to write more. Though I don't feel that I have clarified enough or justified enough.

I shall write you soon about the effect the war has had upon me. I have spoken to you about it, but you have never seemed to take it very seriously. Perhaps seeing in black and white what I feel will affect your opinion of me. Perhaps you will leave me. I accept the challenge. My Hotel Henry experience includes this risk. I got drunk two nights ago. It's hard to believe that I am forty-seven, isn't it?

My love,
Emmy

Now that I have copied this letter into my journal (I had forgotten to make a carbon), I shall take my walk. My scheme included a few weeks of solitude at the Hotel Henry before attempting anything. I did not even intend to write in my journal as soon as I started to, but simply to sit about collecting my thoughts, waiting for the knots of habit to undo themselves.

But after only a week here—two nights ago—I felt amazingly alone and disconnected from my past life, so I began my journal.

My first interesting contact was the salesman in the Blue Bonnet Room. I had heard about this eccentric through my in-laws, the Moores, before I ever came up here. My husband's cousin Laurence Moore told me about him when he heard I was coming. He said: "Take a walk through Grey and Bottle's Department Store, and you'll see a man with a lean red face and reddish hair selling materials by the bolt. That man has an income and is related to Hewitt Molain. He doesn't need to work. He was in my fraternity. Then he disappeared. The next I heard of him he was working there at Grey and Bottle's. I stopped by and said hello to him. For a nut he seemed like a very decent chap. You might even have a drink with him. I think he's quite up to general conversation."

I did not mention Laurence Moore to the society salesman because I thought it might irritate him. I lied and pretended to have been here for months, when actually this is still only my second week at the Hotel Henry. I want everyone to think I have been here a long time. Surely it is not to impress them. Is there anything impressive about a lengthy stay at the Hotel Henry? Any sane person would be alarmed that I should even ask such a question. I ask it because deep in my heart I *do* think a lengthy stay at the Hotel Henry is impressive. Very easy to see that I would, and even sane of me to think it impressive, but not sane of me to expect anyone else to think so, particularly a stranger. Perhaps I simply like to hear myself telling it. I hope so. I shall write some more tomorrow, but now I must go out. I am going to buy a supply of cocoa. When I'm not drunk I like to have a cup of cocoa before going to sleep. My husband likes it too.

* * *

She could not stand the overheated room a second longer. With some difficulty she raised the window, and the cold wind blew in. Some loose sheets of paper went skimming off the top of the desk and flattened themselves against the bookcase. She shut the window and they fell to the floor. The cold air had changed her mood. She looked down at the sheets of paper. They were part of the letter she had just copied. She picked them up: *"I don't feel that I have clarified enough or justified enough,"* she read. She closed her eyes and shook her head. She had been so happy copying this letter into her journal, but now her heart was faint as she scanned its scattered pages. "I have said nothing," she muttered to herself in alarm. "I have said nothing at all. I have not clarified my reasons for being at the Hotel Henry. I have not justified myself."

Automatically she looked around the room. A bottle of whiskey stood on the floor beside one of the legs of the bureau. She stepped forward, picked it up by the neck, and settled with it into her favorite wicker chair.

Going to Massachusetts

Bozoe rubbed away some tears with a closed fist.

"Come on, Bozoe," said Janet. "You're not going to the North Pole."

Bozoe tugged at the wooly fur, and pulled a little of it out.

"Leave your coat alone," said Janet.

"I don't remember why I'm going to Massachusetts," Bozoe moaned. "I knew it would be like this, once I got to the station."

"If you don't want to go to Massachusetts," said Janet, "then come on back to the apartment. We'll stop at Fanny's on the way. I want to buy those tumblers made out of knobby glass. I want brown ones."

Bozoe started to cry in earnest. This caused Janet considerable embarrassment. She was conscious of herself as a public figure because the fact that she owned and ran a garage had given her a good deal of publicity not only in East Clinton but in the neighboring counties. This scene, she said to herself, makes us look like two Italians saying goodbye. Everybody'll think we're Italians. She did not feel true sympathy for Bozoe. Her sense of responsibility was overdeveloped, but she was totally lacking in real tenderness.

"There's no reason for you to cry over a set of whiskey tumblers," said Janet. "I told you ten days ago that I was going to buy them."

"Passengers boarding Bus Number Twenty-seven, northbound. . . ."

"I'm not crying about whiskey tumblers." Bozoe managed with difficulty to get the words out. "I'm crying about Massachusetts. I can't remember my reasons."

"Rockport, Rayville, Muriel. . . ."

"Why don't you listen to the loudspeaker, Bozoe? It's giving you information. If you paid attention to what's going on around

25

you you'd be a lot better off. You concentrate too much on your own private affairs. Try more to be a part of the world.''

* * *

"... *The truth is that I am only twenty-five miles away from the apartment, as you have probably guessed. In fact, you could not help but guess it, since you are perfectly familiar with Larry's Bar and Grill. I could not go to Massachusetts. I cried the whole way up to Muriel and it was as if someone else were getting off the bus, not myself. But someone who was in a desperate hurry to reach the next stop. I was in mortal terror that the bus would not stop at Muriel but continue on to some further destination where I would not know any familiar face. My terror was so great that I actually stopped crying. I kept from crying all the way. That is a lie. Not an actual lie because I never lie as you know. Small solace to either one of us, isn't it? I am sure that you would prefer me to lie, rather than be so intent on explaining my dilemma to you night and day. I am convinced that you would prefer me to lie. It would give you more time for the garage.*''

"So?'' queried Sis McEvoy, an unkind note in her voice. To Janet she did not sound noticeably unkind, since Sis McEvoy was habitually sharp-sounding, and like her had very little sympathy for other human beings. She was sure that Sis McEvoy was bad, and she was determined to save her. She was going to save her quietly without letting Sis suspect her determination. Janet did everything secretly; in fact, secrecy was the essence of her nature, and from it she derived her pleasure and her sense of being an important member of society.

"What's it all about?'' Sis asked irritably. "Why doesn't she raise kids or else go to a psychologist or a psychoanalyst or whatever? My ovaries are crooked or I'd raise kids myself. That's what God's after, isn't it? Space ships or no space ships. What's the problem, anyway? How are her ovaries and the rest of the mess?''

Janet smiled mysteriously. "Bozoe has never wanted a child,'' she said. "She told me she was too scared.''

"Don't you despise cowards?'' said Sis. "Jesus Christ, they turn my stomach.''

Janet frowned. "Bozoe says she despises cowards, too. She worries herself sick about it. She's got it all linked up together with Heaven and Hell. She thinks so much about Heaven and

Hell that she's useless. I've told her for years to occupy herself. I've told her that God would like her better if she was occupied. But she says God isn't interested. That's a kind of slam at me, I suppose. At me and the garage. She's got it in for the garage. It doesn't bother me, but it makes me a little sore when she tries to convince me that I wouldn't be interested in the garage unless she talked to me day and night about her troubles. As if I was interested in the garage just out of spite. I'm a normal woman and I'm interested in my work, like all women are in modern times. I'm a little stockier than most, I guess, and not fussy or feminine. That's because my father was my ideal and my mother was an alcoholic. I'm stocky and I don't like pretty dresses and I'm interested in my work. My work is like God to me. I don't mean I put it above Him, but the next thing to Him. I have a feeling that he approves of my working. That he approves of my working in a garage. Maybe that's cheeky of me, but I can't help it. I've made a name for myself in the garage and I'm decent. I'm normal.'' She paused for a moment to fill the two whiskey tumblers.

''Do you like my whiskey tumblers?'' She was being unusually spry and talkative. ''I don't usually have much time to buy stuff. But I had to, of course. Bozoe never bought anything in her life. She's what you'd call a dead weight. She's getting fatter, too, all the time.''

''They're good tumblers,'' said Sis McEvoy. ''They hold a lot of whiskey.''

Janet flushed slightly at the compliment. She attributed the unaccustomed excitement she felt to her freedom from the presence of Bozoe Flanner.

''Bozoe was very thin when I first knew her,'' she told Sis. ''And she didn't show any signs that she was going to sit night and day making up problems and worrying about God and asking me questions. There wasn't any of that in the beginning. Mainly she was meek, I guess, and she had soft-looking eyes, like a doe or a calf. Maybe she had the problems the whole time and was just planning to spring them on me later. I don't know. I never thought she was going to get so tied up in knots, or so fat either. Naturally if she were heavy and happy too it would be better.''

''I have no flesh on my bones at all,'' said Sis McEvoy, as if she had not even heard the rest of the conversation. ''The whole family's thin, and every last one of us has a rotten lousy temper inherited from both sides. My father and my mother had rotten tempers.''

"I don't mind if you have a temper display in my apartment," said Janet. "Go to it. I believe in people expressing themselves. If you've inherited a temper there isn't much you can do about it except express it. I think it's much better for you to break this crockery pumpkin, for instance, than to hold your temper in and become unnatural. For instance, I could buy another pumpkin and you'd feel relieved. I'd gather that, at any rate. I don't know much about people, really. I never dabbled in people. They were never my specialty. But surely if you've inherited a temper from both sides it would seem to me that you would have to express it. It isn't your fault, is it, after all?" Janet seemed determined to show admiration for Sis McEvoy.

"I'm having fun," she continued unexpectedly. "It's a long time since I've had any fun. I've been too busy getting the garage into shape. Then there's Bozoe trouble. I've kept to the routine. Late Sunday breakfast with popovers and home-made jam. She eats maybe six of them, but with the same solemn expression on her face. I'm husky but a small eater. We have record players and television. But nothing takes her mind off herself. There's no point in my getting any more machines. I've got the cash and the good will, but there's absolutely no point."

"You seem to be very well set up," said Sis McEvoy, narrowing her eyes. "Here's to you." She tipped her glass and drained it.

Janet filled Sister's glass at once. "I'm having a whale of a good time," she said. "I hope you are. Of course I don't want to butt into your business. Bozoe always thought I pored over my account books for such a long time on purpose. She thought I was purposely trying to get away from her. What do you think, Sis McEvoy?" She asked this almost in a playful tone that bordered on a yet unexpressed flirtatiousness.

"I'm not interested in women's arguments with each other," said Sis at once. "I'm interested in women's arguments with men. What else is there? The rest doesn't amount to a row of monkeys."

"Oh, I agree," Janet said, as if she were delighted by this statement which might supply her with the stimulus she was after. "I agree one thousand percent. Remember I spend more time in the garage with the men than I do with Bozoe Flanner."

"I'm not actually living with my husband because of my temper," said Sis. "I don't like long-standing relationships. They disagree with me. I get the blues. I don't want anyone staying in my life for a long time. It gives me the creeps. Men are crazy about me. I like the cocktails and the compliments. Then after a while they turn my stomach."

"You're a very interesting woman," Janet Murphy announced, throwing caution to the winds and finding it pleasant.

"I know I'm interesting," said Sis. "But I'm not so sure life is interesting."

"Are you interested in money?" Janet asked her, "I don't mean money for the sake of money, but for buying things."

Sis did not answer, and Janet feared that she had been rude. "I didn't mean to hurt your feelings," she said. "After all, money comes up in everybody's life. Even duchesses have to talk about money. But I won't, any more. Come on. Let's shake." She held out her hand to Sis McEvoy, but Sis allowed it to stay there foolishly, without accepting the warm grip Janet had intended for her.

"I'm really sorry," she went on, "if you think I was trying to be insulting and personal. I honestly was not. The fact is that I have been so busy building up a reputation for the garage that I behave like a savage. I'll never mention money again." In her heart she felt that Sis was somehow pleased that the subject had been brought up, but was not yet ready to admit it. Sis's tedious work at the combination tearoom and soda fountain where they had met could scarcely make her feel secure.

Bozoe doesn't play one single feminine trick, she told herself, and after all, after struggling nearly ten years to build up a successful and unusual business I'm entitled to some returns. I'm in a rut with Bozoe and this Sis is going to get me out of it. (By now she was actually furious with Bozoe.) I'm entitled to some fun. The men working for me have more fun than I have.

"I feel grateful to you, Sis," she said without explaining her remark. "You've done me a service. May I tell you that I admire your frankness, without offending you?"

Sis McEvoy was beginning to wonder if Janet were another nut like Bozoe Flanner. This worried her a little, but she was too drunk by now for clear thinking. She was enjoying the compliments, although it was disturbing that they should be coming from a woman. She was very proud of never having been depraved or abnormal, and pleased to be merely mean and

29

discontented to the extent of not having been able to stay with any man for longer than the three months she had spent with her husband.

"I'll read you more of Bozoe's letter," Janet suggested.

"I can't wait," said Sis. "I can't wait to hear a lunatic's mind at work first-hand. Her letter's so cheerful and elevating. And so constructive. Go to it. But fill my glass first so I can concentrate. I'd hate to miss a word. It would kill me."

Janet realized that it was unkind of her to be reading her friend's letter to someone who so obviously had only contempt for it. But she felt no loyalty—only eagerness to make Sis see how hard her life had been. She felt that in this way the bond between them might be strengthened.

"Well, here it comes," she said. "Stop me when you can't stand it any more. *I know that you expected me to come back. You did not feel I had the courage to carry out my scheme. I still expect to work it out. But not yet. I am more than ever convinced that my salvation lies in solitude, and coming back to the garage before I have even reached Massachusetts would be a major defeat for me, as I'm sure you must realize, even though you pretend not to know what I'm talking about most of the time. I am convinced that you do know what I'm talking about and if you pretend ignorance of my dilemma so you can increase efficiency at the garage you are going to defeat yourself. I can't actually save you, but I can point little things out to you constantly. I refer to your soul, naturally, and not to any success you've had or to your determination. In any case it came to me on the bus that it was not time for me to leave you, and that although going to Massachusetts required more courage and strength than I seemed able to muster, I was at the same time being very selfish in going. Selfish because I was thinking in terms of my salvation and not yours. I'm glad I thought of this. It is why I stopped crying and got off the bus. Naturally you would disapprove, because I had paid for my ticket which is now wasted, if for no other reason. That's the kind of thing you like me to think about, isn't it? It makes you feel that I'm more human. I have never admired being human, I must say. I want to be like God. But I haven't begun yet. First I have to go to Massachusetts and be alone. But I got off the bus. And I've wasted the fare. I can hear you stressing that above all else, as I say. But I want you to understand that it was not cowardice alone that stopped me from going to Massachusetts. I don't feel*

30

*that I can allow you to sink into the mire of contentment and
happy ambitious enterprise. It is my duty to prevent you from it
as much as I do for myself. It is not fair of me to go away until
you completely understand how I feel about God and my
destiny. Surely we have been brought together for some
purpose, even if that purpose ends by our being separate again.
But not until the time is ripe. Naturally, the psychiatrists would
at once declare that I was laboring under a compulsion. I am
violently against psychiatry, and, in fact, against happiness.
Though of course I love it. I love happiness, I mean. Of course
you would not believe this. Naturally darling I love you, and
I'm afraid that if you don't start suffering soon God will take
some terrible vengeance. It is better for you to offer yourself.
Don't accept social or financial security as your final aim. Or
fame in the garage. Fame is unworthy of you; that is, the desire
for it. Janet, my beloved, I do not expect you to be gloomy or
fanatical as I am. I do not believe that God intended you for
quite as harrowing a destiny as He did for me. I don't mean this
as an insult. I believe you should actually thank your stars. I
would really like to be fulfilling humble daily chores myself and
listening to a concert at night or television or playing a card
game. But I can find no rest, and I don't think you should
either. At least not until you have fully understood my dilemma
on earth. That means that you must no longer turn a deaf ear to
me and pretend that your preoccupation with the garage is in a
sense a holier absorption than trying to understand and fully
realize the importance and meaning of my dilemma. I think that
you hear more than you admit, too. There is a stubborn streak
in your nature working against you, most likely unknown to
yourself. An insistence on being shallow rather than profound. I
repeat: I do not expect you to be as profound as I am. But to
insist on exploiting the most shallow side of one's nature, out of
stubbornness and merely because it is more pleasant to be
shallow, is certainly a sin. Sis McEvoy will help you to express
the shallow side of your nature, by the way. Like a toboggan
slide.''*

Janet stopped abruptly, appalled at having read this last part
aloud. She had not expected Bozoe to mention Sis at all.
''Gee,'' she said. ''Gosh! She's messing everything up
together. I'm awfully sorry.''

Sis McEvoy stood up and walked unsteadily to the television
set. Some of her drink slopped onto the rug as she went. She

faced Janet with fierce eyes. "There's nobody in the world who can talk to me like that, and there's not going to be. Never!" She was leaning on the set and steadying herself against it with both hands. "I'll keep on building double-decker sandwiches all my life first. It's five flights to the top of the building where I live. It's an insurance building, life insurance, and I'm the only woman who lives there. I have boy friends come when they want to. I don't have to worry, either. I'm crooked so I don't have to bother with abortions or any other kind of mess. The hell with television anyway."

She likes the set, Janet said to herself. She felt more secure. "Bozoe and I don't have the same opinions at all," she said. "We don't agree on anything."

"Who cares? You live in the same apartment, don't you? You've lived in the same apartment for ten years. Isn't that all anybody's got to know?" She rapped with her fist on the wood panelling of the television set. "Whose is it, anyhow?" She was growing increasingly aggressive.

"It's mine," Janet said. "It's my television set." She spoke loud so that Sis would be sure to catch her words.

"What the hell do I care?" cried Sis. "I live on top of a life-insurance building and I work in a combination soda-fountain lunch-room. Now read me the rest of the letter."

"I don't think you really want to hear any more of Bozoe's nonsense," Janet said smoothly. "She's spoiling our evening together. There's no reason for us to put up with it all. Why should we? Why don't I make something to eat? Not a sandwich. You must be sick of sandwiches."

"What I eat is my own business," Sis snapped.

"Naturally," said Janet. "I thought you might like something hot like bacon and eggs. Nice crisp bacon and eggs." She hoped to persuade her so that she might forget about the letter.

"I don't like food," said Sis. "I don't even like millionaires' food, so don't waste your time."

"I'm a small eater myself." She had to put off reading Bozoe's letter until Sis had forgotten about it. "My work at the garage requires some sustenance, of course. But it's brainwork now more than manual labor. Being a manager's hard on the brain."

Sis looked at Janet and said: "Your brain doesn't impress me. Or that garage. I like newspaper men. Men who are champions. Like champion boxers. I've known lots of champions. They take to me. Champions all fall for me, but I'd never want any of them to find out that I knew someone like your Bozoe. They'd lose their respect.''

"I wouldn't introduce Bozoe to a boxer either, or anybody else who was interested in sports. I know they'd be bored. I know." She waited. "You're very nice. Very intelligent. You *know* people. That's an asset."

"Stay with Bozoe and her television set," Sis growled.

"It's not her television set. It's mine, Sis. Why don't you sit down? Sit on the couch over there."

"The apartment belongs to both of you, and so does the set. I know what kind of a couple you are. The whole world knows it. I could put you in jail if I wanted to. I could put you and Bozoe both in jail."

In spite of these words she stumbled over to the couch and sat down. "Whiskey," she demanded. "The world loves drunks but it despises perverts. Athletes and boxers drink when they're not in training. All the time."

Janet went over to her and served her a glass of whiskey with very little ice. Let's hope she'll pass out, she said to herself. She couldn't see Sis managing the steps up to her room in the insurance building, and in any case she didn't want her to leave. She's such a relief after Bozoe, she thought. Alive and full of fighting spirit. She's much more my type, coming down to facts. She thought it unwise to go near Sis, and was careful to pour the fresh drink quickly and return to her own seat. She would have preferred to sit next to Sis, in spite of her mention of jail, but she did not relish being punched or smacked in the face. It's all Bozoe's fault, she said to herself. That's what she gets for thinking she's God. Her holy words can fill a happy peaceful room with poison from twenty-five miles away.

"I love my country," said Sis, for no apparent reason. "I love it to death!"

"Sure you do, Hon," said Janet. "I could murder Bozoe for upsetting you with her loony talk. You were so peaceful until she came in."

"Read that letter," said Sister. After a moment she repeated, as if from a distance: "Read the letter."

Janet was perplexed. Obviously food was not going to distract Sis, and she had nothing left to suggest, in any case, but some Gorton's Codfish made into cakes, and she did not dare to offer her these.

33

What a rumpus that would raise, she said to herself. And if I suggest turning on the television she'll raise the roof. Stay off television and codfish cakes until she's normal again. Working at a lunch counter is no joke.

There was nothing she could do but do as Sis told her and hope that she might fall asleep while she was reading her the letter. "Damn Bozoe anyway," she muttered audibly.

"Don't put on any acts," said Sis, clearly awake. "I hate liars and I always smell an act. Even though I didn't go to college. I have no respect for college."

"I didn't go to college," Janet began, hoping Sis might be led on to a new discussion. "I went to commercial school."

"Shut up, God damn you! Nobody ever tried to make a commercial school sound like an interesting topic except you. Nobody! You're out of your mind. Read the letter."

"Just a second," said Janet, knowing there was no hope for her. "Let me put my glasses on and find my place. Doing accounts at the garage year in and year out has ruined my eyes. My eyes used to be perfect." She added this last weakly, without hope of arousing either sympathy or interest.

Sis did not deign to answer.

"Well, here it is again," she began apologetically. "Here it is in all its glory." She poured a neat drink to give herself courage. "*As I believe I just wrote you, I have been down to the bar and brought a drink back with me. (One more defeat for me, a defeat which is of course a daily occurrence, and I daresay I should not bother to mention it in this letter.) In any case I could certainly not face being without one after the strain of actually boarding the bus, even if I did get off without having the courage to stick on it until I got where I was going. However, please keep in mind the second reason I had for stopping short of my destination. Please read it over carefully so that you will not have only contempt for me. The part about the responsibility I feel toward you. The room here over Larry's Bar and Grill is dismal. It is one of several rented out by Larry's sister whom we met a year ago when we stopped here for a meal. You remember. It was the day we took Stretch for a ride and let him out of the car to run in the woods, that scanty patch of woods you found just as the sun was setting, and you kept picking up branches that were stuck together with wet leaves and dirt. . . .*"

"Curls and a quiet country face"

Curls and a quiet country face.

Jennifer-Madeleine. She seems to move in an afternoon light. A brilliantly lighted cold afternoon just before sunset. The melancholy gold color of hayfields from another time, an earlier time, but seen in our day, part of our time. The hay, but not the light. The double heart. Not a drama, but both families. The final painful experience. There must be no more pain like this. Death is better than a long murder.

Might bring into sharper focus what is surrounding and seeming to be outside when the inside is dying. There can be a new joy, a joy so false that one can be shaken with mirth, as one never is, can never be, when the joy is a true one and the inside is not dying.

A play. There comes a moment when there is no possibility of escape, as if the spirit were a box hitting at the walls of the head. Looking at the ocean is the only relief. I have trained my eye to look away from the beach where they are going to build the new docks. I cannot look at that part of the beach unless I think of my own end, curtail my own sense of time, as Paul says that we must all do now. I can do it, but it's like: "You too can live with cancer." When I was little I had to imagine that there was some limit to physical pain in order to enjoy the day. I have never yet enjoyed a day, but I have never stopped trying to arrange for happiness. My present plan to get Tetum into my house is as good as any other. It is at a very pleasant stage of development—still like a daydream. Nothing has changed. My father predicted everything when he said I would procrastinate until I died. I knew then it was true. In America it was terribly painful to know this as a child. Now that I am nearly forty and in North Africa it is still painful.

A play. Is it writing I'm putting off, or was it always something else—a religious sacrifice? The only time I wrote well, when I passed through the inner door, I felt guilt. I must find that again. If I can't, maybe I shall find a way to give it up. I cannot go on this way.

I love Tangier, but like a dying person. When Tetum and Cherifa die I might leave. But we are all three of us the same age, more or less. Tetum older, Cherifa a bit younger. I'd like to buy them meat and fish and oil so that they will stay alive longer. I don't know which one I like best, or how long I can go on this way, at the point of expectation, yet knowing at the same time that it is all hopeless. Does it matter? It is more the coming home to them that I want than it is they themselves. But I do want them to belong to me, which is of course impossible. I must try to stop thinking of them. Best to spend a month or two at Madame de Marquette's. The hardest time is now.

AT THE
JUMPING BEAN

"At the Jumping Bean" is a scene from a play
Jane Bowles was writing in Ceylon in 1955.

The interior of The Jumping Bean. Booths, colored paper lanterns. The bar will be supplied with bottles as well as with hamburgers and ketchup. Over the doorway there is a neon sign reading THE JUMPING BEAN, *which the audience sees backward. Over the bar is a list written in huge letters:*

★★★★★★★★★★★★★★★★★★★★★★★★★★★★★★★★★★★★★★★

Bean Burgers . . . Our Jumping Specials. Unique.
Complete Chicken Dinners $1.33
Extra Cole Slaw Cup Free . . . "For them what likes it."
Free Jumpers with every order.

BEANAROO COCKTAIL. *"Swig it down. Then Jump."* . . . .55 cents.

★★★★★★★★★★★★★★★★★★★★★★★★★★★★★★★★

BERYL JANE and GABRIEL are seated at a table. She is dressed in a very feminine, pert manner.

Beryl Jane: They have such tiny little chickens here.

Gabriel: Yes, but they don't cost much.

Beryl Jane: I know.

Gabriel: Maybe it's foolish to try and eat chicken at this price.

Beryl Jane: The other kids do. They love them.

Gabriel: They're busy dancing and flirting. That's why they come here to the Jumping Bean. To dance and flirt. I guess most of the guys buy these little chicken dinners more for show than they do for eating. If guys were alone they'd just stuff themselves on beanburgers and fill up. Some of them do anyhow. Even with a girl along, guys who are low on cash. And some guys who don't give a damn about showing off to a girl, don't care what impression

39

they make on a girl. A lot of them don't even bother talking. Some of them don't even *like* girls.

Beryl Jane: Those are pansies.

Gabriel: They come in here, too.

Beryl Jane: [*Thinking of the cabin she has rented*] What do they order?

Gabriel: [*Talking through his hat*] I guess they don't bother with much. They don't sit down to a table and order the dollar thirty-three, I don't guess. They have beers at the bar, and maybe beanburgers. They don't bother much. They're kind of without girls, and folks frown at them.

Beryl Jane: There's everything in this world. Everything under the sun. But you can't spend your whole life worrying about other people.

Gabriel: Some people do. They worry about humanity.

Beryl Jane: I worry about reality.

Gabriel: What do you mean?

Beryl Jane: I mean everything that's close to me, that's real. Like my father and my projects, and . . . and . . . my front porch, the swing, and especially my own room, and science. Science is close to me.
[*She hesitates.*]
It really is. If I start thinking about far-off things, or things that are too different, then I get, like, paralyzed. I get off the track. Like kids thinking about eternity when they're little. We all hated it.

Gabriel: We hated eternity?

Beryl Jane: But you have to think about those things more than I do, because you're a poet.
[*The chicken dinners arrive and they stop talking while the waitress lays out the various plates.*]
They really are small chickens, aren't they? They're smaller than they were last time.

Waitress:	But you've got five different items come with that chicken plate. You've got chips, greens, Juliennes, Parkers, and the slaw cup.
	[She holds up the tiniest possible paper cup. Beryl Jane and Gabriel look up at it.]
	If you feel like you want your extra slaw cup right off I can bring it to you now. It's coming free with the dollar thirty three.
	[Pointing to the list over the bar.]
	''For them what likes it.''
	[She reads this in a dull routine voice. She has obviously no spirit of fun in her at all.]
	And here's your jumpers.
	[She tosses some jumping beans onto the table.]
	They come free with all items, down to cokes.
Gabriel:	We don't want any jumping beans. We want to talk and eat.
Waitress:	*[ignoring his request]* We're open all night.
Gabriel:	You can have another dollar thirty three if you want, Beryl Jane. If you're still hungry when you finish this one.
Beryl Jane:	You're not a millionaire, Gabriel.
Gabriel:	If I was a millionaire I'd be travelling. I wouldn't be buying these little chicken dinners.
Beryl Jane:	If everything works out with the pigs the way it should, we'll have enough money to travel for two months out of the year. Switzerland or Paris. Or we could go and see the Northern Lights, or museums. Then, back home.
	[She eats for a moment.]
	You'd have your room upstairs for writing poetry. You'd come back from a trip full of inspiration. All those beautiful sights . . . *[Gabriel laughs.]*
	. . . And you'd be real glad to be home in your own house . . . in your own room.
	[Her own deep unexpressed fear that none

41

*of this will come true communicates
itself to the audience.*]

We'll leave some of our land wild, with just natural pastures and woods. Your windows, Gabriel. . . .

[*She searches his face, but she is not sure he is listening.*]

While you're writing your poetry you can look out the window at the wild beautiful land. The kind of land you always say you like.

[Gabriel *continues eating. He looks very sad.*]

And the equipment and the buildings and the pigs. They'll all be on the other side of the house. You won't even know they're there. It will be just like you were off in a log cabin with nobody around. No pigs . . .

Gabriel: I don't mind pigs. I like them.

Beryl Jane: Well, maybe you don't like them around all the time. Anyway, not when you're writing poetry.

Gabriel: I don't care. They can all come into my room if they want to. Maybe I won't write poetry.

[*He looks very defeated.*]

Beryl Jane: The pigs aren't going to walk in and out of the house. It's going to be a very modern farm.

Gabriel: Can't we stop talking about the future? Why don't we dance?

[*He gets up and goes over to the juke-box. It starts to play.*]

Beryl Jane: I love the future. Except when it looks black. Pop says if the world blows up it won't be my fault. But he gets sore if he doesn't think I'm concentrating on my course. He says I should think about people all over the world and crises a normal amount, but he wants me to tend to my own business and follow my goal. He hates people who are wishy-washy, who don't know what they're doing. You know, like should I or shouldn't I.

42

Gabriel: He must be nuts about me.

Beryl Jane: I told him you were interested and getting very excited about pig farming. I told him that you were a writer besides. He asked me if you wrote facts and I said you did.

> [*They dance for a moment.*]

Gabriel. . . .

Gabriel: What?

Beryl Jane: What time are we going to go back to the cabin?

> [*They stop dancing and stand still in the middle of the floor.*]

It's because you've got so much on your mind all the time. You might forget . . . about the cabin. I don't think we should go there so late that we're both so tired, you know.

> [*She stops and looks at him, a very peculiar expression on her face. She seems almost frozen, but she is compelled to go on. Then, in a strange childish voice:*]

I get so tired at night. It's because I get up so early. I get so tired.

> [*He doesn't answer. His eyes are blank.*]

Like a kid, isn't it? I'm like a little girl?

> [*There must be something terrifying about this scene. Her smile is crooked, as if she were being trampled inside.*]

Don't you think so?

> [*An almost repulsive innocence.*]

I still play marbles with my brother. And I climb apple trees.

Gabriel: Do you?

Beryl Jane: Yes. Maybe you do, too.

Gabriel: No. I don't.

Beryl Jane: Maybe I'll climb apple trees even after I have a baby. People don't get so old any more. My aunt's forty and she plays pool all the time. When it's summer she goes crabbing.

[He is silent.]

There's nothing much to having a baby any more, even. They get 'em walking right off, the mothers, I mean. I'll bet my aunt would get up and play pool the day after her baby was born, if she had a baby. But she's frigid.

[She sits down.]

Are we going?

Gabriel: I'm going to get a drink. Do you want one?

Beryl Jane: Yes. I'll have a drink.

Gabriel: [calling]
Waitress! Two drinks!

Waitress: Two beanaroo cocktails?

Gabriel: Two whiskeys. And don't bring those jumping beans.

Waitress: No jumpers? They come . . .

Gabriel: I don't want any jumping beans with my drink. That's enough jumping beans.

Beryl Jane: [In panic embarrassment, but with a drive to get to the cabin no matter what, because she has planned it that way.]
Why are you so sore about the jumpers? You can just leave them alone. Just leave them alone on the table if you don't want to play with them.

Gabriel: Why do they treat us like kids on these routes? It's the same way at Larry's Devilburger.

Beryl Jane: [Pale, as if he were insulting her.]
They have no jumping beans.

Gabriel: They've got four cages with those little mice inside them, running up and down ladders like maniacs and swinging themselves.

Beryl Jane: They're not mice. They're hamsters. Everybody loves them. Even people's grandparents.

Gabriel: And the Routeburger.

44

Beryl Jane:	They've got nothing. Nothing but the extra slaw cup free. That's the same as here, but no other attractions. An extra paper slaw cup and Juliennes and Parks and greens and dancing. They've got the dollar thirty three but no jumpers.

[She stops and looks at him. Gabriel has drained his drink and wears a black look on his face.]

Gabriel?

Gabriel:	What?

Beryl Jane:	If you don't like these joints we don't have to come to them. I don't care about them.

[He shrugs his shoulders.]

But I *am* beginning to feel tired, like I said. I'm more like a child than most girls. I like cocoa at night, and bread and jam. I like a child's dinner, not a grown-up dinner. If I'm alone . . . Boy! I go straight for the cocoa and soft-boiled eggs and toast. I don't really give a damn about whiskey.

[Gabriel takes her glass and finishes off her drink.]

Beryl Jane:	Now? Gabriel, shall we pay our check and go now? I'll go stand in the doorway while you pay the check.

[Gabriel goes to the bar.]

Gabriel:	*[to the Waitress]* Give me the check and I'll pay here.

Waitress:	I can bring the check to your table. There's no need for you to come here. You got table service.

Gabriel:	I don't want to go back to my table. I want to pay here.

Waitress:	You're kind of contrary, aren't you?

[Gabriel shrugs.]

I've got a nephew who's contrary. Name is Norman. He came like that. Interferes with his making a living. He thinks nothing of sitting and letting the women work. Just so long as he can go on being his own contrary self. If he didn't come straight out of my only sister I'd boot him in the ass. He and I don't greet unless it's a calendar holiday. Then we greet because it looks too bad if we don't. But we make it short. He knows he's sitting on my sister while I'm bending my elbow at the Beanburger.

> [Gabriel *leaves the bar angrily, and stands next to* Beryl Jane. *They are framed in the doorway.*]

Gabriel: There's no moon, Beryl. It's very dark out.

Beryl Jane: I know. But there are lights all along the highway.

Gabriel: Don't you like the moon, though?

Beryl Jane: I don't know. Not as much as some people. I never think about looking up unless someone says: Beryl, look at the moon! When I'm by myself I never look at the moon. I don't know. I guess I'm not too keen on it.

Gabriel: Well, what do you like?

> [*There is a stillness to the scene. The restaurant lights darken, and they are illuminated only by the blue light of the upside down neon sign. Their faces look white.*]

Beryl Jane: What do I like?

Gabriel: What beautiful sight? I mean, without travelling. What do you think is beautiful?

Beryl Jane: I like . . . I like tea-roses. And . . .

> [*She falters.*]

Do you mean anything that's beautiful?

Gabriel: Yes. You never mention much what you think is beautiful.

Beryl Jane:
> [*very quickly, spontaneously, with sparkle and life*]

I think snakes are beautiful. Those snakes with diamonds on their backs and very dark colored scales, deep green and purple and black.

Gabriel: [*uncomprehending*]
        Snakes.

Beryl Jane: Yes, snakes. Some snakes anyway.
        [*She looks at him. He has moved away
        from her. Panic rising again.*]
        Maybe that's not the kind of beautiful thing you
        meant. Maybe you didn't want to hear about
        snakes. Maybe you meant more like what beautiful
        things do I love that the world loves.

                        [*He does not answer.*]

        I told you, Gabriel. Tea-roses. And there are other
        things, but I don't want to talk about them now.
        Not in front of The Jumping Bean. I can't think
        here. And don't tell anybody I like snakes. I don't
        want people to think. . . .
                [*He has begun to walk. She stands still an
                instant, and then starts after him.*]

A SELECTION
OF PHOTOGRAPHS

THE PHOTOGRAPHS

a. *Jane (Woodmere, L.I., circa 1929)*

b. *Jane with Truman Capote (Tangier, August 1949)*

c. *Seated group on divan, left to right: Unidentified man, unidentified woman, Comtesse della Faille, Jane, unidentified man (Tangier, August 1949)*

d. *Jane and Paul Bowles (Tangier, August 1949)*

e. *Standing group, left to right, Gene Chavez, Lilla van Saher, Captain of S.S. "Queen Frederica," Tennessee Williams, Jane, John Goodwin, First Mate of S.S. "Queen Frederica" (At sea, May 1956)*

f. *Jane (Tangier, May 1960)*

g. *Jane (Tangier, May 1960)*

h. *Jane and Paul Bowles (Arcila, July 1963)*

i. *Jane (Arcila, July 1963)*

a.

b.

c.

d.

e.

f.

g.

h.

i.

SIX LETTERS

Katharine Hamill and Natasha von Hoeschelmann were for many years on the staff of Fortune *magazine. "Bupple" is Paul Bowles, as is "Paul." Libby Holman was a musical comedy star of the 'twenties; she was the original "torch singer."*

1

[Taghit, Algeria
Spring 1949]

Dearest Katharine and Natasha:

I can't tell you everything that's happened because if I tried to I wouldn't write at all. I *have* tried to before, and simply stopped writing because it was too exhausting. No one could have been happier than I was to receive your Xmas wire. It was wonderful to know you'd thought of me. (I sound like a real cripple or a public charge.) Certainly you were the only ones who did. Then I started many grateful letters and Jody was with me and it was all very complicated. Now I am in the Sahara desert. I got to Marseille in February, stayed four days and came back to Africa. Scared to go to Paris because there is a very long tunnel outside of Marseille. Lola can appreciate this. Of course I'm not neurotic any more, which is a good thing, but I do find it very hard to go *North*. This place we're in is an oasis—a very small one. We had to walk to it from the bus, with donkey carriers for our luggage. It is not a bus, but a very interesting and solidly built *truck* that goes to Timbuctoo. The dunes are extremely high, and I shall not attempt to climb them again. Well, maybe I will. Because it's so beautiful up there. Nothing but mountains and valleys of sand as far as the eye can see. And to know it stretches for literally hundreds of miles gives a very strange feeling. The sand is a wonderful beige color. It turns bright pink in the evening light. I am impressed. It is not like anything else anywhere in the world, not the sand and the oasis, anyway. The rest is all rocks and rather terrifying. We saw a mirage called *Lake Michigan and the New Causeway* on our way here. I suppose there are mirages in New Mexico, but I can't remember. We are going on to Beni Abbes (Paul and I), next Friday. The hotel here is kept up for the army, since no tourists

63

ever come. Occasionally army people stop by for lunch. There are just Paul and me, the Arab who runs the hotel, the three soldiers in the fort, and the natives. But *they* are just a little too native, and frightfully underfed. It is very very quiet. No electricity, no cars. Just *Paul* and *me,* and many empty rooms. The great sand desert begins just outside my window. I might almost stroke the dune with my hand. We are going further "in." (Oy!) But I am looking forward to the next place, though I doubt that it will be as beautiful as this oasis. Nothing could be. The little inn where we'll be going is run by a woman, a Mademoiselle Jury. Paul says she's a yenty old maid. I think there are eight or nine "whites" there—a real mob. Paul thinks there will be too much traffic because the truck goes through twice a week. There is no road leading *here* at all, so he's gotten used to that. We plan to be in the desert about a month, and then back to Fez. Then to Tangier, where I can resume my silly life with the grain market group: Tetum, Zodelia, Cherifa and Kinza. You remember them. I had Tetum x-rayed. She was determined to go to the doctor's because I'd taken Cherifa ten times about her foot. Tetum spent all morning in the doctor's waiting-room among the women wrapped in sheets. She was happy because she had caught up with Cherifa. She felt that the x-ray equalled the foot treatments Cherifa got out of me. It is all really about prestige, their life. But I cannot tell them even that I know they are making an ass out of me. I am always afraid they might find out I know. I'll tell you about it when I see you.

Forgive this disjointed letter, please. I have had a fly after me, and then in the middle of it the Arab who runs the hotel asked me to write a letter for him. (Naturally he can't write.) It was to a man living in a place called *Oil Tin Number Five.* It's a famous hellhole south of here. I hope we don't go there to live. Write me British Post Office, Tangier. If I'm still here they'll forward the mail.

Much love as ever,
Jane

2

17th Jan. [1950]
Paris

Dearest Bupple,

I suppose I should single-space this, though I hate to. There is
no room for corrections. I shall get all the disagreeable things off
my mind first. My work went well last week. I had got into a
routine, but this week it's all shot to hell again . . . not because
of my life really, but because I have come to the male character
again. I must change all that I wrote about him in Tangier. Not
all, but it must become real to me, otherwise I can't write it. I
have decided not to become hysterical, however. If I cannot
write my book, then I shall give up writing, that's all. Then
either suicide or another life. It is rather frightening to think of.
I don't believe I would commit suicide, though intellectually it
seems the only way out. I would never be brave enough, and it
would upset everybody. But where would I go? I daresay the
most courageous thing to do would be nothing. I mean, to
continue as I am, but not as a writer. As the wife of a writer? I
don't think you'd like that, and could I do it well? I think I'd
nag and be mean, and then I would be ashamed. Oh, what a
black future it could be! That is why I have to use some control,
otherwise I get in a panic. I am trying to write. Jody's being
here is a hindrance and a help. A help because she gives a center
to my day, and a hindrance because if I read, and wrote the
letters I should write, and simply wandered around chewing my
cud as one does when one's writing, I would have very little
time left for her. We have been seeing too many people . . . not
many different ones, but the same few over and over again.
There have been very few dinners alone, and it has taken me
some weeks to realize that Jody just doesn't want to have

anyone much around. Though if they must be around, she prefers them to be men. Gordon she likes, and Frank Price. I have miraculously avoided a real bust-up drama, and have kept the most severe check on myself. I think now that things are well adjusted, and I am clear in my mind about how to conduct the rest of the winter until she leaves: in solitary confinement as much as possible. Strange that when she first arrived I thought we had a whole lifetime together; I guess that threw me into a panic. And now I feel I've done it all wrong. It would have been pleasanter and better for my work seeing no one else (the strain of wondering whether she was enjoying an evening or not gave me a headache), and instead getting into the habit of eating dinner in silence (unless I talk) which is, after all, not so bad. I don't know what I was afraid of. Despair, I guess, as usual. Now there seems to be not enough time left. I have grown used to her again, and fond of her, and we have moved into Frank Price's flat, which will be much better. I had taken my own room on the other floor because our room was not suitable for working; and because of a scene she made about my "walking out" on her, I felt guilty every time I was in my room and was not strictly working. She later explained how she felt, and tried to reassure me that she no longer felt that way about it, yet I could never be in my own room with any serenity. The fairies on the other side of the wall drove me crazy anyway, and turned out to be almost as bad as the children in the courtyard who had made work impossible for me in the room we had shared together (the same arrangement you and I had). It wasn't big enough anyway for actual living, though it was fine just for a week.

I want desperately to get another "clump" of work done in the next four or five weeks. There is simply no time for anything, ever. I know that I shall be terribly upset when she leaves. There will be a week of agony, I suppose. Changing from this charming flat into a cheap room, financial insecurity which I don't have now, and so on. I am sending you O.'s letter so that you know what's going on. If this option does get to me, instead of tearing up roots again, I may spend part of the spring in Paris . . . how long I don't know. I may also go to Tangier, depending on whether you're there or not and a few other un-predictables. If however the play does go into rehearsal this sum-mer, I *would* prefer, as Oliver suggests, to go back in July rather than in the spring. It would be better sailing, would give me longer to work on Yenti, if I'm still working by then, and

I'd see you sooner, as I'd most likely get down to Africa eventually.

I see Alice Toklas now and then, but I'm afraid that each time I do I am stiffer and more afraid. She is charming, and will probably see me less and less as a result of my inability to converse. This is not a result of my shyness alone, but of a definite absence of intellect, or should I say of ideas that can be expressed, ideas that I am in any way certain about. I have no opinions really. This is not just neurotic. It is very true. And Alice Toklas gives one plenty of opportunity to express an idea or an opinion. She is sitting there waiting to hear one. She admires your book tremendously. In fact, she talked of little else the last time I saw her. She won't serve me those little bread sandwiches in different colors any more because she says I like them more than the cake, and so eat them instead of the cake. I do like them better. And now I must go there and eat only sweets, which makes me even more nervous. Maybe she'll never speak to me again. Eudora Welty came over to dinner with Mary Lou Aswell and told me she was a great admirer of yours. She asked for *Camp Cataract* and took it home with her. After nearly a month she returned it with a note explaining that she failed on it, but would like to try something else of mine some day. I had met her on the street in the middle of the month, and she said then that she was having trouble with it, and so she never did finish it. I was disturbed by that as I have, since seeing you last, turned into an admirer of hers, and it would be nice for me to be admired by an established and talented American writer, instead of by my friends and no one else. That was upsetting, and also the fact that a friend in the hotel didn't like it really. (A very brilliant and charming girl called Natika Waterbury, who is now in Paris but whom I met long ago in New York.) This evening Sonia Sekula is giving a small party in her room. Mary Reynolds will come, and Lionel Abel and Pegeen. (Pegeen has two babies, apparently by her husband Hélion.) Jody will attend, perhaps, but I can't, because I am dining with, of all people, Sidéry, who was very excited when he heard I was your wife. I met him at one of the few cocktails I've been to, at Peggy's. He is quite charming, I think. I wrote you about Manchester, but you must simply have forgotten. I gave him to Truman, not because T. wanted him (though if he did it was for my sake, not his) but because I didn't like his face or his nature when I returned. Though Donald was never a real Peke, he was cute from the very first minute, and this one was cute only because he was a little fluffy ball. His muzzle had gotten much whiter, and his face definitely more pointed, and his eyes closer together. I thought I had better give him away while I disliked his looks, as I'm sure he would have been a nuisance. I have a few clippings which I'll enclose, though I'm sure you have them already. The book, though second from the bottom, made the best-seller list, which I think is wonderful. Your literary success is a fact now, and it is not only distinguished but widespread. I think to have Connolly and Toklas and a host of other literary people, plus a public, is really remarkable and wonderful. You should soon write another book. I hope that you are pleased at last, and not simply because it is a way to make some money. You do deserve a success of this kind, and I think you are at the right age for it. I can get no news out of anyone in Tangier. Have written Ira and Jacqueline and the fact that I hear from no one confirms me in my belief that Esterhazy has gone. It is rather horrid not knowing what is going on. I am glad I have a little money down there because if anyone ever writes me I should like to send checks for Fathma. I have just about nothing left here, and I know this will horrify you, but it just happened, and without my going to nightclubs either. I am waiting from day to day for the option money to arrive from Audrey Wood via Oliver, rather than send for more from Tangier. Naturally I would have been more careful if I hadn't had a letter from Wood that sounded pretty definite about the option. *Blondes* is not only a hit but a smash hit. Laurence Olivier's head reader saw my play and wrote that it was morbid and depressing, and though not something to be dismissed, certainly nothing they could think of doing. Truman hates New York, and wrote: "Honey, even if your play is done I hope you won't have to come back for it." Alice T. was delighted that you didn't really care for him very much. (I told her.) She said it was the one thing that really worried her. She could not understand how an intelligent person like you etc. She doesn't seem to worry in the least, however, about my liking him. So I'm insulted . . . again.

Paris is so very beautiful, particularly in this dark winter light. I'm surprised you don't love it more. I still love Africa best I guess, but there one must shut one's eyes against a great many things too. Here there is the Right Bank, and there the Villes Nouvelles, the buses, and the European shoes. You know what I mean. To cross the river never ceases to excite me. I went to see *Phèdre* at the Comédie Française with Natika. I am wildly excited about it. The only thing I have enjoyed thoroughly in years. I have never heard French *grand théâtre* before. I don't know how good the players were, but one must be good to do Racine at all. I shall go there now as often as possible.

I have gotten rounder in the face from the nourishing food. I'm upset about it, but perhaps it is becoming. Poor Michael Duff's son was born dead. I don't hear from them. Just a funny postcard now and then. I am terribly sorry that I can't give you more information about your book. Certainly friends in New York can do better. I might as well be in Ceylon with you. I love the descriptions of it, by the way, though at the moment I feel no need of adding any country to my list. I am puzzled enough with the Seine River and the Grand Socco. Oddly enough I still love Morocco best, though I do not admire it more. I think and think about what it means to me, and as usual have come to no conclusion. I dream about it too, in color, all the time.

Much much love, Bupple dear. I miss you very much. Write me your plans and don't stay away forever. I hope you'll return sometime this spring. Will you?

P.S. I had my tooth fixed. The dentist hurt like hell. Is Gore really joining you?

3

[1954]

Darling Natasha and Katharine:

I never stop thinking about you, but too much has happened. Please forgive me if this is not an amusing letter. I think I had better simply write you a gross factual résumé of what has happened. Then if I have any sense I shall keep notes. Because what is happening is interesting and funny in itself. I am a fool to have lost two whole months of it. I have no memory—only a subconscious memory which I am afraid translates everything into something else, and so I shall have to take notes. I have a very pretty leather book for that purpose.

The day you left I was terribly, terribly sad. . . . I went down that long street, way down in, and landed in a room filled with eighteen women and a dozen or two little babies wearing knitted capes and hoods. One lady had on a peach satin evening dress and over it the jacket of a man's business suit. (A Spanish business-suit.) I had been searching for Cherifa, and having been to three houses all belonging to her family, I finally landed there. I thought I was in a bordello. The room was very plush, filled with hideous blue and white chenille cushions made in Manchester, England. Cherifa wore a pale blue sateen skirt down to the ground, and a grayish Spanish sweater, a kind of school sweater, but not sporty. She seemed to be constantly flirting with a woman in a blue kaftan (our hostess). Finally she sat next to her and encircled her waist. Cherifa looked like a child. The woman weighed about 160 pounds and was loaded with rouge and eye makeup. Now I know her. An alcoholic named Fat Zohra, and one of two wives. She is married to a kind of criminal who I believe knifed his own brother over a card game and spent five years in jail. The other wife lives in a different house and does all the child-bearing. Fat Zohra is barren. There was one pale-looking girl (very light green), who I thought was surely the richest and the most distinguished of the lot. She wore a wonderful embroidered kaftan, a rich spinach green with a leaf design. Her face was rather sour: thin compressed lips and a long mean-looking nose. I was sad while they played drums and did their lewd belly dances, because I thought: My God, if you had only stayed a day longer. But of course if you had, perhaps they wouldn't have asked you in; they are so leery of strangers. In any case, at the end of the afternoon . . . Cherifa took me to the doorway and into the blue courtyard where two boring pigeons were squatting, and asked me whether or not I was going to live in my house. The drums were still beating and I had sticky cakes in my hand . . . those I couldn't eat. (I had stuffed down as many as I could; I loathe them) but I was really too sad because you had left to get down very many. I said I was (going to live in the house) but not before I found a maid. She told me to wait and a minute later came out with the distinguished pale-green one. "Here's your maid," she said. "A very poor girl."

Anyway, a month and a half later she became my maid. I call her Sour Pickle, and she has stolen roughly about one thousand four hundred pesetas from me. I told C. about it. She advised me not to keep any money in the house. She is a wonderful maid, an excellent cook, and sleeps in.

Paul had typhoid in the hotel, and that was a frightening mess for two weeks. We were both about to move into our houses. He had found one on a street called Sidi Bouknadel (overlooking the sea) and I was coming here. Then he had typhoid, and then Tennessee came for two whole weeks. I moved in here while Paul was still in the hotel. For a while Ahmed and I were living together while Paul lingered on at the hotel in a weakish state. He is all right now. Ahmed stayed here during the month of Ramadan (the month when they eat at night) and I was with him during the last two weeks. Not very interesting, except that every night I woke up choking with charcoal smoke, and then he would insist that I eat with him, liver or steak or whatever the hell it was. At first I minded terribly. Then I began to expect it, and one night he didn't buy really enough for the two of us, and I was grieved. Meanwhile in the daytime I was in the hotel preparing special food for Paul, to bring his appetite back. There were always four or five of us cooking at once in the long narrow hotel kitchen, the only room that looked out on the sea. Meeting Tennessee and Frankie for dinner was complicated, too. (They were at the Rembrandt.) Synchronizing took up most of the time. We were all in different places.

One day before Ramadan and before Paul had paratyphoid, I went to the market and sat in a gloom about Indo-China and the Moroccan situation and every other thing in the world that was a situation outside my own. Soon I cheered up a little. I was in the part where Tetum sits in among the coal and the mules and the chickens. Two little boy musicians came by. I gave them money and Tetum ordered songs. Soon we had a big crowd around us, one of those Marrakech circles. Everybody stopped working (working?) and we had one half hour of music, myself and everybody else, in that part of the market. And people gathered from round about. Just like Tiflis. Tetum was in good spirits. She told me that Cherifa had a girl friend who was fat and white. I recognized Fat Zohra, though I shall never know whether I put the fat white picture in her mind or not. I might have said: "Is she fat and white?" I don't know. Then she asked me if I wouldn't drive her out to Sidi Menari, one of the sacred groves around here where Sidi Menari (a saint) is buried. They like to visit as many saints as possible, of course, because it gives them extra gold stars for heaven. I thought: "Natasha and Katharine will be angry. They told me to stick to Cherifa, but then, they didn't know about Fat Zohra." After saying this in my head I felt free to offer Tetum a trip to the grove without making you angry.

Of course it turned out that she wanted to take not only one, but two, neighbors and their children. We were to leave at eight thirty A.M., she insisted. The next day when I got to Tetum's house on the Marshan, with Temsamany (nearly an hour late) Tetum came to the door in a grey bathrobe. I was very surprised. Underneath she was dressed in a long zigdoun, and under that she wore other things. I can't describe a zigdoun, but it is quite enough to wear without adding a bathrobe. But when they wear our nightclothes they wear them over or under their own (which are simply the underpeelings or first three layers of their day clothes. Like in Tiflis.). She yanked me into her house, tickled my palm, shouted to her neighbor (asleep on the other side of a thin curtain) and in general pranced about the room. She dressed me up in a hideous half-Arab, half-Spanish cotton dress which came to my ankles and had no shape at all. Just a little round neck. She belted it, and said: "Now go back to the hotel and show your husband how pretty you look." I said I would some other day, and what about our trip to the saint's tomb? She said yes, yes, but she had to go and fetch the two other women who both lived in other parts of town. I said would they be ready, and she said something like: "bacai . . . shouay." Which means just nothing. Finally I arranged to come back for her at three. Rather infuriated because I had gotten Temsamany up at the crack. But I was not surprised, nor was he. Tetum took me to her gate. "If you're not here at three," she said in sudden anger, "I shall walk to the grove myself on my own legs." (Five hours, roughly.) We went back at three, and the laundry bags were ready, and the children, and Tetum.

"We are going to two saints," Tetum said. "First Sidi Menari. And then we'll stop at the other saint's on the way back. He's buried on the edge of town and we've got to take the children to him and cut their throats because they've got whooping-cough." She poked one of the laundry bundles, who showed me a knife. I was getting rather nervous because Paul of course was expecting us back roughly around seven, and I know how long those things can take. We drove along the awful road (the one that frightened you) toward the grove, only we went on and on, much further out, and the road began to bother me a little after a while. You would have hated it. The knife of course served for the symbolic cutting of the children's throats, though at first I had thought they were going to draw some blood, if not a great deal. I didn't think they were actually going to kill the children or I wouldn't have taken them on the ride.

We reached the sacred grove, which is not far from the lighthouse one can see, coming into the harbor. Unfortunately they have built some ugly restaurants around and about the lighthouse and not far from the sacred grove, so that sedans are now constantly passing on the highway. The grove itself is very beautiful, and if one goes far enough inside it, far away from the road, one does not see the cars passing. We didn't penetrate very far into the grove because being a Christian (Oy!) I can't get to the vicinity of the saint's tomb. Temsamany spread the tarpaulin on the ground and the endless tea equipment they had brought with them, and they were off to the saint. He said: "I shall make a fire, and then when they come back the water will be boiling."

They came back. God knows when. The water was boiling. We had used up a lot of dead olive branches. They sat down and lowered their veils so that they hung under their chins like ugly bibs. They had brought an excellent sponge cake. As usual, something sweet. I thought: "Romance here is impossible." Tetum's neighbors were ugly. One in particular. "Like a turtle," Temsamany said. She kept looking down into her lap. Tetum, the captain of the group, said to the turtle: "Look at the world, look at the world." "I am looking at the world," the other woman said, but she kept looking down into her lap.

They cut up all the sponge cake. I said: "Stop! Leave it. We'll never eat it all." Temsamany said: "I'm going to roller-skate." He went off and we could see him through the trees. After a while the conversation stopped. Even Tetum was at a loss. There was a little excitement when they spotted the woman who takes care of the toilets under the grain market, seated not far off with a group somewhat larger than ours. But nothing else happened.

I went to look for Temsamany on the highway. He had roller-skated out of sight. I felt that all my pursuits here were hopeless. I looked back over my shoulder into the grove. Tetum was swinging upside-down from an olive tree, her knees hooked over a branch, and she is, after all, forty-five and veiled and a miser.

There is more to this day. But I see now that I have done exactly what I did not want to do. I have gone into great detail about one incident which is probably of no interest.

I always let Fatima (Sour Pickle) decide what we are to eat. It is all so terribly simple, all in one dish. Either lamb with olives or with raisins and onions, or chicken with the same, or ground meat on skewers, or beef or lamb. (You remember how wonderful they taste.) Or a fried potato omelet with onions, or boiled noodles with butter, and always lots of black bread and wine at five pesetas a quart. (Excellent.) I've had guests once . . . Tennessee, in fact: white beans in oil and with salt pork, like the ones I cooked for you. Lots of salad, cucumber, tomato and onion all chopped up, almost daily. Fresh figs, bananas, cherries . . . whatever is in season. Wonderful bowls of Turkish coffee in the morning, with piles of toast soaked in butter. At noon we eat very little. I go over to Paul's for lunch, except that he never eats until three thirty . . . sometimes four. I get up at seven, and by then I am so hungry I don't even care, but I like seeing him. We eat soup and bread and butter and cheese and tunafish. For me tunafish is the main diet. I love this life and I'm terrified of the day when my money runs out. Please write. I shall worry now about this messy letter.

All my love, always,
J. Bowles

4

❈ ❈ ❈ ❈ ❈ ❈ ❈

[1955]
Tangier

Dearest Bupple:

It has been very difficult for me to write you. I have covered sheet after sheet, but now I am less troubled in my head for some reason. Maybe because I hit bottom, I think. And now I feel that the weight is lifting. I am not going back in that wild despairing way over my departure from Ceylon, my missing the end of your novel, the temple of Madura, that terrible trip back alone (a nightmare to the end because it was the twin of the other trip I might have made with you). It was better toward the end, but I hit bottom again in Tangier. The house reeked of medicine and there was the smell of other people's stale soup in the velvet *haeti* and even in the blue wall. I put my nose on the wall. It was cold and I could smell soup. The first day I was in the house the whole Casbah reeked of some sweet and horrible chemical smell which doubled its intensity with each new gust of the east wind. The Arabs were holding their noses, but I didn't know that. On the first day I thought I alone could smell it, and it was like the madness I had been living in. A nightmare smell coming up from the port, and a special punishment for me, for my return. I really felt very bad. I can't even remember whether or not Cherifa came to me here that first night in the house. Truly, I can't. On the second day the barber came over to me in his white and black hood and asked me to go to the Administration about the smell. He was holding his nose. "There are microbes in the air. We will all perish," he said. As he spends his entire time in the mosque and is one of the few old-fashioned Arabs left in the quarter, I was amused. The smell is gone now. The sewer pipes had broken, and they were dumping some chemical into the sea while they were mending them. And from that day on I felt better. And the house smells better—at least, to me. Fathma said: "Naturally. Filthy Nazarene cooking. Everything made of pork. Pork soup, pork bread, pork coffee, an all-pork house." But now there is kaimon, and charcoal, in the air. I feel so much better. But I am terrified of beginning to work. I don't know what I'll do if that nightmare closes in on me again. I am sorry too that you have to live through it. I won't go near you if it happens again. Actually I cannot allow it to happen again. But I must work. I had some shattering news when I returned . . . *le coup de grâce* . . . my taxes. Clean out of my mind from the first second that I banked the money. Somewhere way back, someone, either you or Audrey, warned me not to consider the money all mine, and I was a fool to forget. Having never paid taxes. . . . However, I suppose it is understandable. The slip of paper doesn't say much, not even what percent I am to be taxed. Perhaps all that has gone off to you. In view of the condition I was in this winter and on the boat, I should think this blow would have landed me in the hospital. In fact I went to bed and waited. But I got up again the next day alive and sane still, though my head was pounding with blood-pressure symptoms. I had to get out of that state, obviously, and I did. I tried writing you, but the letters were *magillahs,* and all about Madura and the tax and Mrs. Trimmer and Cherifa in one *tajine.* Senseless and anguished, and they weighed a ton. Not the moment to start that, if I am to "resort to airmail." Anyway, I think I have enough money in the bank to cover the tax, and if not, I have a Fabergé gold bracelet. And I have (if I must sell it, and if Oliver has made full payment on it) my beautiful Berman painting. Naturally, if I had known this was going to be waiting for me I would not have returned, because surely I should like to have discussed the thing with you. It's a terrible bore writing about it. There are so many angles to it: what exemptions I can get . . . maybe a lot . . . maybe none. Is it best to get off the double income-tax and pay direct to the government, or should I pay to you? Anyway, for God's sake don't do anything about it until you see me. I shall wait in Tangier and I shall lead my life as if it would go on. I cannot face the possibility of its not going on. Yet I would be unwilling to stay here if it meant your giving up Temsamany and the car. I consider them essentials, just as there seem to be essentials to my life here without which I might as well be somewhere else. Maybe I'll have to be, but it is best to face that when it comes, in two months or with luck, later. I have pulled every string possible in the sense of looking for a job. I can only do it through friends. There is a terrible depression in Tangier. Hotels empty, the Massilia closing, and ten people waiting for every job. Most people think I am mad, and that I should write or live on you, or both. It is not easy to make friends take my plight seriously. Not easy at all, unless I were to say that I was starving to death, which would be shameful and untrue. I spent just a little too much in every direction. The top floor expenses in New York which I took over for a few months, taxis, restaurants, coming over travelling with Natasha and Katharine, the Rembrandt, the Massilia, extravagances with C., I suppose more dinner parties than I need have given, doctors here for myself and Fathma. I don't know . . . it went in every direction. But each thing separately is a drop in the bucket. It is just everything put together in the end. I suppose I've been bad, but not so bad. Please don't scold; I am miserable enough about the whole thing and would have pinched every penny as I am doing now, had I been less confident. Well, that is over the bridge and down the drain, like the money for Ceylon. But although Ceylon was wasted and I did not see the temples, or even Kandy, it has changed my life here to a degree that is scarcely believable. I very swiftly reduced expenses to a scale so much lower than anything C. has ever expected of me when I was here that she is at the moment back in the grain market. I think it is a healthy thing for C. to go to the market in any case, even if the funds were more adequate. Ramadan she will be going there a lot.

I am now exhausted. Ramadan would be an ideal time for me to escape to New York, I suppose, but I don't want to, until I know that I can come back here or that I can't, at least, not for a while—that is, if we are both too broke. I'll face that later too. If I go downhill again then I suppose I would go home. Finding it impossible to work again is the only thing I fear . . . the hell with Ramadan. I am rather grateful that C. does want to go to the market during that time. Because she can't come here in a straw hat, but must keep going back to the bottom of Emsallah to change into a veil and white gloves, it will be difficult for her to come regularly. And what with fasting, etc. She's been fasting now for two weeks. Hopscotch off and on, making up time. It's almost worse than real Ramadan. I am thinking of investing in a room I heard of, on the top floor of the Hotel

Cuba. I will count it outside my budget, since it is not a permanent thing, but something I would like to try, just so I can get started working. Naturally when I first got back and realized about my taxes I was too accablée to do any work . . . too harassed, and still in that funny state. I think the room is a good idea, if it is still there. I have not seen it yet. But I will look at it. I can ask Mother to give it to me as a special present, or if it works out I shall simply keep it on as an outlet for as long as it does work out. Because that would mean I was working. As for C. and all that, I shouldn't even bother writing you about her since it is such a fluctuating uncertain quantity. At the same time I feel this terrible compulsion to write you about the geographical location of the grain market in relation to Emsallah and my house, and the awful amount of travelling she would have to do if she went often to the market during Ramadan, just to get in and out of her straw hat. I doubt that she will go often once the *aïd* is over, but we'll see. I certainly do not wish to interfere with her work, ever (!). I have no right to, since my own position here is so precarious, and in any case I shouldn't. She has now expressed a desire to travel and to play tennis. Now I do have an upper hand that I never had when I spent more money. What is it? I suppose one must close one's fist, and allow them just the right amount of money to make it worthwhile and not shameful in the eyes of the neighbors. I understand many more of the family problems than I did. It was difficult before to find one's way in the maze. But for "the moment," I know that is over. Will explain when I see you, maybe, if I don't forget to. I'm sure you can't wait. I remember the glazed look you always got when I mentioned her before. I think however if that nonsense began again I would give up. If I could only work now I would feel quite peaceful.

Tangier looks worse. The Socco in the afternoon is mostly filled with old clothes. A veritable flea-market that I'm trying to preserve. I've been booming away at Phyllis about it, because she knows the new Administrator. I also asked her about my hair. She has me down on a list. It says: Janie, Grand Socco, hair. Which is just about it, isn't it? The same obsessions, over and over. When I am sure about my hair I will write. But I think the news is good. You will never know what that nightmare was like. I know you thought it was in my mind. I am going on with Bépanthène Roche. On the days I buy it I try to eat more cheaply, so that I can keep, as much as I can, within a budget.

Phyllis gave me a blue bead for luck and to ward off the evil eye. Brion's restaurant is the only thing that does business in town. John Goodwin invited me to go to Spain any time during the Feria and Holy Week. He has an apartment for a month. But I'm not sure that the trip alone wouldn't come to a thousand pesetas or more. Also I never go anywhere, so why should I suddenly get to the Feria, since I didn't get to Madura. I would like to hear some Gypsies, but not with those tourists there. I do not think I will go. And certainly not if I'm working.

My terrace smells of male pipi. I suppose it will forever. Eric Gifford brought his male cat with him, Hassan, whom he never mentioned to me. Or else I wasn't paying attention. The worst of the bad weather is over, although the first two weeks at the Massilia were hell. Temsamany scared me so on the boat, about people being able to stay in one's house forever, that I offered them two weeks' grace in the house. I wrote you that I cheered up on the boat when I thought of George Jantos, and sure enough having him as a neighbor has made a lot of difference to me. I rather like their little group, and they are so near I can pop in there. He is bringing me some kif today. I had a cigarette of kif last night before supper and rather liked the effect. I had some drinks too, so I don't suppose I can judge, but it changed the effect of the drink noticeably.

I had dinner with Fathma, who is staying on for three hundred a month instead of five hundred, full-time as before. They have both been cooperative about buying cheap food, and C. of course is in her element. But then, that was before she decided to go back to the market.

The baqals announced a three-day close-down in commemoration of the upset here two or three years ago, and they were closed one. *Plus ça change.* Now my left hand is tired. Please write, and especially about your book, and don't above all scold me or put me in a panic. We'll talk about it all when you come, if you ever do. I wonder if instead you'll go to England? Anyway, Bubble, I think the trip has done some good. Much love. I hope you are well and that it got really hot. Write everything.

Jane

5

<hr />

February 1957
Tangier

Dear Paul:

I have just had my fortieth birthday the day before yesterday, and that is always, however long one has prepared for it, a shock. The day was not as bad as the day after it, or the following day, which was even worse. Something coming is not at all like something which has come. It makes trying to work that much more difficult (or could it possibly be more difficult?), because the full horror of having no serious work behind me at this age (or successful work, in any sense) is now like an official fact rather than something in my imagination, something to be feared, but not yet realized. Well, I don't suppose you can understand this, since when you reached forty you had already quite enough stacked up behind you.

I realized about your birthday, but I don't think I mentioned it in my letters, or thought of it at the time I wrote you. Anyway, it is over. I did not tell anyone about mine except Cherifa, and I celebrated with her on the night of the twenty-first because on the twenty-second an old man from Xauen, an uncle or grandfather, was expected at her house. However, Christopher heard about it from George and called me on the twenty-second to ask if it were true, and then I did have a busy day. I sound like your mother about to say that Ulla came over and that they took a drive and later popped corn in the grate. In spite of hating it to be forty (Anne Harbach toasted me and said: "Life begins . . ." which was the last straw), I am still determined to write my play, and have no intention of going back to New York until my money runs out. I have somehow, thus far, staved off the terrible depression that was coming over me when I wrote you last—staved it off perhaps simply because I cannot ever again be the way I was in Ceylon. I mean that I will do everything in my power to pretend that I am not, even if I am. It was too horrible. And so I knocked off work entirely for a week and then went back to trying to write the play. My mind is not a total blank, which is more than I can say of the way it was before. Whether it will get beyond that, I don't know. I am sure you will come out all right because you always have.

Seth said his first word yesterday. "Dubz." He said it clearly three times, and again this morning. I daresay it is because Seth sits in the bathroom a lot and I am always lunging in after Dubz to stop him from using the tub, and of course calling out: "Dubz!" at the top of my lungs. I hope that he will keep saying it so you will hear him when you get back.

Mr. Rothschild has been here for three days and I like him. He is giving me a subscription to the Sunday Times for a year, and it will be delivered to me from New York by boat of course, so it will always be two weeks late. It is for Berred and Dubz, for their pans.

Radiant sunshine, balmy weather and scarcely any rain. The beaches are crowded. I had lunch with Mr. Mallan at the Catalana last week. The Mar Chica is booming again. Whether or not there are many Arabs in it I don't know. Apparently there is more drink than ever in their world, only not as openly. There seems to be not much fear about. Ramadan is in less than forty days, and I dread it as usual. Seth is so terribly noisy that I have to put him out on the terrace in order to do any work. I am furious that you are living in Colombo and have an oscillating standing fan. I would have loved that. If you like Weligama so much why don't you keep it . . . or aren't you prepared to live alone there? Actually I don't think you would like that for long. But maybe you won't be able to sell it. Your life in Colombo doesn't sound too expensive thank God so I imagine you'll stay there until you sell the house. Seth is driving me mad.

Dubz just fell into the toilet up to his waist and I had to help him to dry off. Mr. Mallan after beating around the bush for fifteen minutes finally asked me what color eyes Phyllis della Faille has. He is utterly ridiculous. Please write me about him. Cherifa bought Seth a length of strong wire which she has fastened around his cup and the bars of his cage so that he can no longer dump his seeds on the floor. It is to be a great saving in money and I am glad. He just said "Dubz" again. I try to say it over and over again to him so that he won't forget.

Much love, J.

82

6

[circa 1958]

Dearest Libby:

I am very sad not to have written you. It is too much of a task evaluating the whole situation and then writing what is important and what isn't. I can write down all my worries, and there are roughly about eleven major ones, including a very faint worry—not a worry actually, but an *awareness* that this is after all earthquake country, although we are not on the Agadir fault. That was such a nightmare. The reports on Agadir came here daily, and to top it off we had a tremor here. The people were so hysterical that they slept in the bullring all night. The Jews especially. I didn't know about it until the next morning. It is not fair to mention only the other worries since that one obsessed me for a good two months. Anyway, most of them will hold until I see you. But when will I see you? You write as if Paul and I were likely to go back to America together, or as if he would go back at all. He announced last night that he would have to see his parents eventually (I suppose within the next five years), which surprised me. So perhaps he will go back. I did not think that he would ever set foot in the United States unless it was to work. There don't seem to be any jobs for him any more now that he has so cut himself off from the market place in New York. He is more and more forgotten (even by Tennessee) unless it is simply that incidental music is too expensive and hardly worth importing someone to the States for, because of the fare. He would probably get more jobs if he lived in some accessible place, but naturally he wouldn't. And besides, his living expenses would be more, although they have trebled here in the last two and a half years. Many things are more expensive than they are in New York. Things have changed considerably, but I don't think there will be a revolution this year (according to my spies) and maybe not for many more years, depending on what happens in the rest of the world, naturally. I shall ask your permission not to mention politics. I don't like them any more.

The doctor does not want me to stay alone because of the danger that I might have a fit in the street or fall down and hit my head. I have a Spanish woman because she can keep accounts. My most solemn worry is about my work, and above all, do I really have any? Can I ever have any again? I will try to settle it this summer and next fall. (Within the next six or eight months.) For myself, anyway, because it has nothing to do with anyone else. Also there is nothing new except that I don't always know which is the stroke and which is the writer's block. I know some things have definitely to do with the stroke, and others I'm not sure of. The sheep festival is about to begin, in a month, and they are all buying their sheep now for the slaughter. I think that I will not be able to buy a sheep this year. They are too expensive for me, and Cherifa is having four teeth pulled, and later, a bridge made.

I have trouble with names, numbers, and above all the ability to add and subtract. I know perfectly well the general outlines. Two hundred dollars is less than three hundred dollars, and ten plus ten equals twenty, but the complicated divisions and subtractions and additions—! Adding more than two figures is impossible for me. That can be relearned, but I really need someone with me in this country, or they would all cheat me because I could not correct their own sums which are *always wrong*. So Angèle does that. I suppose that is the least of my worries, but I'm sure that none of this is psychosomatic, because I have no mental block about numbers, and they are worse than the rest. I don't think it would take more than six months to relearn the whole multiplication table. It is very funny but not bad, because I know what I need to know, and then can have someone else do the work. Some women are bad at computing even without strokes, and they are not as charming as I am. Don't ask Dr. Resnick anything. He might have discouraging news, and above all I must for once in my life keep my hopes up. Paul says that he spoke to the doctors and they said that nobody knew how much one could improve or how long it would take. The doctor in New York who sent me to that ghastly young man at Lenox Hill—I forget his name— said the hemianopsia was permanent, but not the aphasia, which has proved to be correct. I now know the meaning of all words. They register again on my brain, but I am slow because there is a tiny paralyzed spot in each eye which I apparently have to circumvent when I'm reading. One side is very bad, worse than the other, but on the whole I'm getting much more used to it. Don't say anything to Resnick because he can't possibly predict anything, and anyway he is apt to be frank, and maybe he would say something depressing. Undoubtedly. I have an awful feeling that I've written this whole thing before. I will send the blood pressure readings and ask if there are any new drugs besides serpasil. My own doctor is pleased with me.

Libby, there is so much talk about myself in this letter that I think I must stop. I have left half the things out that I wanted to tell you about. At least there are no politics in this one. I was fairly poetic in the old days.

Much love,
J.

ABOUT JANE BOWLES

Jane Sidney Auer was born in New York City on February 22nd, 1917. Her childhood was spent in Woodmere, Long Island, where she attended public school. Her secondary education was continued at Stoneleigh. A fall from a horse there put an end to this period of her life. The following year she entered a hospital at Leysin, Switzerland, where she remained in traction for two years. During this time she was tutored intensively by a French Professor who introduced her to the works of Gide. She began a novel in French (*Le Phaeton Hypocrite*) which she completed in New York in 1935. It was never published, and the typescript has disappeared.

In 1937 she met Paul Bowles and went to Mexico with him, along with the Dutch painter Tonny and his wife. The next year she and Bowles were married. They spent several months in Central America, and continued to Paris, finally taking a house on the Côte d'Azur. At this point Jane had already begun to work on a novel which was finished in Mexico in 1941 as *Two Serious Ladies*. Knopf accepted the book in 1942, and it was published in the Spring of 1943.

In New York, at the suggestion of Oliver Smith, she began to write a play. The writing of *In the Summer House* occupied her from 1944 until the end of the road tour of the Playwright's Company production at the close of 1953. (Prior to this there had been two trial productions, the first at the Hedgerow Theatre in Philadelphia, and one at Ann Arbor, Michigan, starring Miriam Hopkins.)

She saw Tangier first in 1947, and always preferred it to the other Moroccan cities, in spite of the fact that she wrote very little there beyond the fragments appearing in the present volume. In the *Collected Works,* only "Everything is Nice" was written in Tangier. "Camp Cataract" dates from Fez in 1948, and "A Stick of Green Candy" from the Sahara in 1949.

She began to have difficulty writing in the 'fifties, mainly because she had become hypercritical of her work. In 1957 she suffered a cerebral haemorrhage which destroyed half her field of vision. Reading and writing became almost impossible for her. From then on, her health declined slowly, and she was in and out of hospital over a period of sixteen years. She died on May 4, 1973, in Málaga, Spain.

P. B.

Printed April 1976 in Santa Barbara &
Ann Arbor for the Black Sparrow Press by
Mackintosh & Young and Edwards Brothers Inc.
Design by Barbara Martin. This edition is
published in paper wrappers; there are
500 hardcover trade copies; & 50 numbered
copies have been handbound in boards by
Earle Gray.